MIDDLE-GRADE MATH MINUTES

One Hundred Minutes to Better Basic Skills

Written by
Doug Stoffel

Editor
Alaska Hults

Illustrator
Corbin Hillam

Cover Illustrator
Rick Grayson

Designers
Moonhee Pak and Mary L. Gagné

Cover Designer
Barbara Peterson

Art Director
Tom Cochrane

Project Director
Carolea Williams

Reprinted 2011
© 2000 Creative Teaching Press, Inc., Huntington Beach, CA 92649

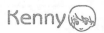

TABLE OF CONTENTS

INTRODUCTION

The focus of *Middle-Grade Math Minutes* is math fluency—teaching students to solve problems effortlessly and rapidly. The problems in this book provide students with practice in every key area of middle-grade math instruction, including

- basic multiplication and division facts
- money
- graphing
- problem solving
- measurement
- fractions
- place value
- time
- pre-algebra
- the vocabulary of mathematics
- geometry

Use this comprehensive resource to improve your students' overall math fluency, which will promote greater self-confidence in their math skills as well as provide the everyday practice necessary to succeed in a testing situation.

Middle-Grade Math Minutes features 100 "Minutes." Each Minute consists of ten classroom-tested problems for students to complete in one minute. Each Minute includes questions of varying degrees of difficulty, integrating problem solving and basic math skills. This unique format offers students an ongoing opportunity to improve their own fluency in a manageable, nonthreatening format. The quick, one-minute format combined with instant feedback makes this a challenging and motivational assignment students will look forward to each day. Students become active learners as they discover mathematical relationships and apply acquired understanding to complex situations and to the solution of realistic problems in each Minute.

How to Use This Book

Middle-Grade Math Minutes is designed to be implemented in numerical order. Students who need the most support will find the order of skills as introduced most helpful in building and retaining confidence and success. For example, the first time that students are asked to provide the value of pi to the hundredths place, the digits in the ones and tenths places are provided. The second time, the digit in the ones place is provided. It is not until the third time that students are asked the value of pi that they must recall the number without additional support.

Middle-Grade Math Minutes can be used in a variety of ways. Use one Minute a day for warm-up activities, bell-work, review, assessment, or a home-work assignment. Keep in mind that students will get the most benefit from their daily Minute if they receive immediate feedback. If you assign the Minute as homework, correct it in class as soon as students are settled at the beginning of the day.

If you use the Minutes as a timed activity, place the paper facedown on the students' desks or display it as a transparency. Use a clock or kitchen timer to measure one minute. Encourage students to concentrate on completing each problem successfully and not to dwell on problems they cannot complete. At the end of the minute, have students stop working. Then, read the answers from the answer key (pages 108–112) or display them on a transparency. Have students correct their own work and record their score on the Minute Journal reproducible (page 6). Then, have the class go over each problem together to discuss the solution(s). Spend more time on problems that were clearly challenging for most of the class. Tell students that difficult problems will appear on future Minutes and they will have another opportunity for success.

Teach students strategies for improving their scores, especially if you time their work on each Minute. Include strategies such as

- leave more time-consuming problems for last
- come back to problems they are unsure of after they have completed all other problems
- make educated guesses when they encounter problems they are unfamiliar with
- rewrite word problems as number problems
- use mental math wherever possible

Students will learn to apply these strategies to other timed-test situations.

The Minutes are designed to improve math fluency and should not be included as part of a student's overall math grade. However, the Minutes provide an excellent opportunity for you to see which skills the class as a whole needs to practice or review. This knowledge will help you plan the content of future math lessons. A class that consistently has difficulty with reading graphs, for example, may make excellent use of your lesson in that area, especially if they know they will have another opportunity to achieve success in this area on a future Minute. Have students file their Math Journal and Minutes for that week in a location accessible to you both. You will find that math skills that require review will be revealed during class discussions of each problem. However, you may find it useful to review the Minutes on a weekly basis before sending them home with students at the end of the week.

While you will not include student Minute scores in your formal grading, you may wish to recognize improvements by awarding additional privileges or offering a reward if the entire class scores above a certain level for a week or more. Showing students that you recognize their efforts provides additional motivation to succeed.

MINUTE JOURNAL

NAME _____

MINUTE	DATE	SCORE	MINUTE	DATE	SCORE	MINUTE	DATE	SCORE	MINUTE	DATE	SCORE
1			26			51			76		
2			27			52			77		
3			28			53			78		
4			29			54			79		
5			30			55			80		
6			31			56			81		
7			32			57			82		
8			33			58			83		
9			34			59			84		
10			35			60			85		
11			36			61			86		
12			37			62			87		
13			38			63			88		
14			39			64			89		
15			40			65			90		
16			41			66			91		
17			42			67			92		
18			43			68			93		
19			44			69			94		
20			45			70			95		
21			46			71			96		
22			47			72			97		
23			48			73			98		
24			49			74			99		
25			50			75			100		

Middle-Grade Math Minutes © 2000 Creative Teaching Press

Scope and Sequence

MINUTE 1

NAME _____

1. 6 x 3 =

2. How many ears do eight dogs have in all? _____

3. If $n + 2 = 7$, then $n =$

4. There were eight bugs on the ground. Now there are six. How many flew away? _____

5. 2 x 3 x 2 =

6. 4 x 6 + _____ = 31

7. 3, 6, 9, 12, _____, _____, _____

8. Seven bicycles have _____ wheels in all.

Use <, >, or = to complete questions 9 and 10.

9. 3 weeks _____ 20 days

10. 1 cm _____ 1 in.

Middle-Grade Math Minutes © 2000 Creative Teaching Press

MINUTE 2

NAME _____

1. $3 \cdot 5 =$

2. Four dollars equal _____ pennies.

3. $2 + 5 \cdot 2 =$

4. $5 + 8 - 3 =$

5. $\dfrac{6}{2} =$

6. 0, 4, 8, 12, _____, _____, _____

7. $0 \times 5{,}132 =$

8. $2\overline{)32}$

9. The <u>product</u> of four and three is _____.

10. The <u>sum</u> of five and four is _____.

MINUTE 3

NAME _____

1. The <u>product</u> of 4 and 6 is _____.

2. $2,463 \times 0 =$

3. 1, 10, 2, 9, 3, _____, _____, _____

4. $\frac{8}{4} =$

5. $4\overline{)48}$

6. $8 + 6 \div 3 =$

7. $3 + 4 \cdot 3 =$

8. How much does <u>each</u> apple cost? _____

9. $5 + (3 - 1) =$

10. The <u>difference</u> between 9 and 5 is _____.

MINUTE 4

NAME _____

1. 1, 5, 9, 13, _____, _____, _____

2. $10 - 4 \cdot 2 =$

3. $\dfrac{18}{3} =$

4. $84 \div 1 =$

5. Does Ellen spend more time on homework or sports? _____

6. $4 \cdot 3 + 5 \cdot 1 =$

For questions 7–10, use $a = 2$, $b = 3$, and $c = 6$.

7. $a + b =$

8. $ac =$

9. $\dfrac{c}{a} =$

10. $2b =$

MINUTE 5

NAME _____

For questions 1–5, use $a = 8$, $b = 2$, and $c = \dfrac{1}{2}$.

1. $a + b =$

2. $b + c =$

3. $ab =$

4. $ca =$

5. $4a =$

6. $\dfrac{14}{2} =$

7. 1, 2, 4, 8, _____, _____, _____

8. The <u>sum</u> of 8 and 7 is _____.

9. The <u>difference</u> between 9 and 3 is _____.

10. $10 - 3 \bullet 3 =$

Middle-Grade Math Minutes © 2000 Creative Teaching Press

MINUTE 6

NAME _____

1. $4 \cdot 4 =$

2. $5^2 =$

3. $2 \cdot 2 \cdot 2 =$

4. Which number is in both A and B? _____

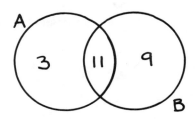

5. $10 - 5 \cdot 2 =$

6. $6^2 =$

7. $1 \cdot 1 \cdot 1 \cdot 1 =$

8. $\dfrac{10}{5} =$

9. Circle the answer that is equal to $5 \cdot 5 \cdot 5$:
    a. 5 x 3   b. 3 x 5   c. 5^3 d. 3^5

10. $3 + 5 =$

MINUTE 7

NAME _____

1. $8^2 =$

2. $4^2 - 6 =$

3. A trio and a quartet got together and played a song. How many musicians were there? _____

4. $2 + 3 \cdot 3 + 2 =$

5. $2 \overline{)36}$

6. $10^2 =$

7. $\frac{1}{2} \cdot 10 =$

8. $3 \cdot 2 \cdot 1 =$

9. Circle the answer that is equal to 4^3:
   a. $4 \cdot 4 \cdot 4$ b. $4 \cdot 3$ c. $4 + 3$ d. $3 \cdot 3 \cdot 3 \cdot 3$

10. $\frac{4}{2} =$

Middle-Grade Math Minutes © 2000 Creative Teaching Press

MINUTE 8

NAME _____

1. $3^2 =$

2. $\dfrac{18}{3} =$

3. Circle the answer that is equal to 5^3:
   a. 5×3 b. $3 \cdot 3 \cdot 3 \cdot 3 \cdot 3$ c. 3×5 d. $5 \cdot 5 \cdot 5$

4. If $8 + y = 15$, then $y =$

5. $15 + 3 \cdot 2 =$

6. Scott ate half of the pizza.
   How many pieces did he eat? _____

7. $\begin{array}{r} 35 \\ \times\, 35 \\ \hline \end{array}$

8. $\dfrac{1}{2} \times 12 =$

For questions 9 and 10, use $a = 5$ and $b = 2$.

9. $ab =$

10. $ba =$

MINUTE 9

NAME _____

1. $7^2 =$

2. If $4r = 24$, then $r =$

3. $\dfrac{15}{3} =$

4. $5(4 + 2) =$

5. $6 + 4 \cdot 2 =$

6. If $s - 8 = 9$, then $s =$

7. $\begin{array}{r} 45 \\ \times\ 45 \\ \hline \end{array}$

8. $2^3 =$

9. If there are fifty dimes in a roll of coins, then it is equal to _____ dollars.

10. The <u>product</u> of eight and nine is _____.

Middle-Grade Math Minutes © 2000 Creative Teaching Press

MINUTE 10

NAME _____

1. $\frac{1}{2}(20) =$

2. $\frac{20}{4} =$

3. $(4 + 4)^2 =$

4. The <u>quotient</u> of $3\overline{)27}$ is _____.

5. One half of fifty is _____.

6. 128, 64, 32, 16, _____, _____, _____

7. $256 \cdot 0 =$

For questions 8–10, use $a = 5$, $b = 4$, and $c = 2$.

8. $ac =$

9. $2a =$

10. $\frac{b}{c} =$

MINUTE 11

NAME _____

1. If $a + 15 = 19$, then $a =$

2. If $b = 2$, then $b^3 =$

3. $8(4 + 3) =$

4. $10 + 4 \times 2 =$

5. Five cars have how many wheels altogether? _____

6. If $3n = 18$, then $n =$

7. $50 \times 50 =$

8. Eight squared is _____.

9. If $y - 4 = 11$, then $y =$

10. What time is shown on the clock? _____

Middle-Grade Math Minutes © 2000 Creative Teaching Press

MINUTE 12

NAME _____

1. The <u>sum</u> of four and twelve is _____.

2. Six ducks have how many feet in all? _____

3. $(8 - 3)^2 =$

4. $\frac{1}{2} \times 16 =$

5. Three squared is _____.

6. $8 \cdot 1 + 4 \cdot 2 =$

7. $8 - 3 \cdot 2 =$

8. Five dollars equal how many pennies? _____

9. If $a = 5$, then $a^2 =$

10. Four weeks is _____ days.

MINUTE 13

NAME _____

1. $3(4 + 2 + 1) =$

2. If 6 pennies are in each pile, how many pennies are in nine piles? _____

3. $9 - $ _____ $= 3$

4. $7 \times 4 =$

5. $12 - 3 \cdot 4 =$

6. $8(10) =$

7. If $65 + a = 71$, then $a =$

8. Twenty-four divided by eight is _____.

9. If $a = 9$, then $5a =$

10. Twelve quarters equal _____ dollars.

MINUTE 14

NAME _____

1. $15 - 3 \cdot 2 =$

2. $25 \div 5 =$

3. $3^3 =$

4. A <u>centi</u>pede has _____ legs.

5. $(5 + 4)^2 =$

6. _____ $- 4 = 4$

7. Forty nickels equal _____ dollars.

Use <, >, or = to complete questions 8–10.

8. 3^2 _____ 24

9. 1 meter _____ 100 millimeters

10. $9(8)$ _____ $8(5 + 4)$

MINUTE 15

NAME _____

1. $4 \times 4 =$

2. Five boxes of pencils with ten pencils per box equal _____ pencils.

3. If $18 \div 3 = n$, then $n =$

4. $70 \times 70 =$

5. The <u>product</u> of 6 and 3 is _____.

6. $2^2 +$ _____ $= 9$

7. 1, 4, 9, 16, _____, _____, _____

8. $\frac{15}{3} =$

9. Five tricycles have _____ wheels.

10. Five squared plus ten is equal to _____.

Middle-Grade Math Minutes © 2000 Creative Teaching Press

MINUTE 16

NAME _____

1. 8 x 4 =

2.
$$\begin{array}{r} 65 \\ \times\ 65 \\ \hline \end{array}$$

3. 10(12) =

4. Three centuries equal _____ years.

5. Five squared is equal to _____.

6. 7 + (4 • 2) =

7. $3\overline{)45}$

For questions 8–10, use $a = 4$, $b = 9$, and $c = 3$.

8. $ac =$

9. $\dfrac{b}{c} =$

10. $5b =$

MINUTE 17

NAME _____

1. $7^2 =$

2. $10 - 5 + 3 =$

3. $0.6 + 0.3 =$

4. Six weeks is equal to _____ days.

5. $18 - 6 \cdot 2 =$

6. What time is shown on the clock? _____

7. $12 \div 2 \div 2 =$

Use <, >, or = to complete questions 8–10.

8. 0.55 _____ 0.65

9. 0.083 _____ 0.81

10. 0.6 _____ 0.60

Middle-Grade Math Minutes © 2000 Creative Teaching Press

MINUTE 18

NAME _____

1. $3(4 + 1 + 2) =$

2. Order these numbers from least to greatest:
5.2, 0.052, 0.52 _____, _____, _____

3. $2^3 =$

4. $\dfrac{20}{4} =$

5. Circle the greater number: 0.0853   or   0.09

6. Circle the answer that is equivalent to 4^3:
a. 12   b. 4 • 4 • 4   c. 3 • 3 • 3 • 3   d. 43

7. The <u>product</u> of 8 and 11 is _____.

Use <, >, or = to complete questions 8–10.

8. 4.03 _____ 4.01

9. 0.0034 _____ 0.03

10. 10.6 _____ 10.600

MINUTE 19

NAME _____

1. $0.8 - 0.5 =$

2. Circle the greatest number: 0.55   0.50   0.505

3. Circle the number with the least value: 0.092   0.029   0.043

4. If $a = 9$, then $a^2 =$

5. If $3x = 27$, then $x =$

6. Three feet equal _____ inches.

7. $3 + 9 \cdot 2 =$

8. Order these numbers from least to greatest:
0.08, 8.0, 0.8 _____, _____, _____

9. A field goal is worth three points. The Bears have kicked four field goals. How many points is this altogether? _____

10. $3 \times 2 \times 4 =$

Middle-Grade Math Minutes © 2000 Creative Teaching Press

MINUTE 20

NAME _____

1. If $a + 8 = 16$, then $a =$

2. Circle the greatest number: 8.20   8.02   8.022

3. $0.3 + 0.2 + 0.1 =$

For questions 4–7, round to the underlined place value.

4. 2<u>6</u>.26 _____

5. <u>2</u>.81 _____

6. 0.0<u>1</u>8 _____

7. 15.<u>4</u>5 _____

For questions 8–10, use $a = 2$, $b = 3$, and $c = 8$.

8. $ac =$

9. The <u>sum</u> of a and b is _____.

10. $\dfrac{c}{a} =$

MINUTE 21

NAME _____

1. $0.8 + 0.6 =$

2. If $\dfrac{x}{3} = 6$, then $x =$

3. Circle the number with the least value: 0.051   3.82   0.05

4. Ten weeks equal _____ days.

5. $10 - 6 + 2 =$

6. $3^2 + 2 =$

7. Eight dogs have _____ legs in all.

For questions 8–10, round to the underlined place value.

8. 0.787 _____

9. 0.506 _____

10. 2.8 _____

Middle-Grade Math Minutes © 2000 Creative Teaching Press

MINUTE 22

NAME _____

1. $\begin{array}{r} 55 \\ \times\, 55 \\ \hline \end{array}$

2. $8 - 3 + 4 =$

3. Sixteen quarters equal _____ dollars.

4. $6(8) =$

5. $\dfrac{28}{4} =$

6. If $g - 4 = 18$, then $g =$

7. If $a = 3$, then $2^a =$

For questions 8–10, estimate the answer by rounding to the ones place and then applying the correct operation. Number 8 is done for you.

8. $12.2 + 4.9 = \mathbf{12 + 5 = 17}$

9. $18.9 - 3.6 =$

10. $6.9 \times 8.2 =$

MINUTE 23

NAME _____

1. $4^2 =$

2. The <u>product</u> of 6 and 3 is _____.

3. Circle the answer that is equal to 3 • 3 • 3 • 3:
   a. 4^3 b. 3^4 c. 3^3 d. 12

4. $5(3+5) =$

Use <, >, or = to complete questions 5–7.

5. 4.1 _____ 6

6. 2.08 _____ 2.080

7. 5.03 _____ 5.4

For questions 8–10, round to the underlined place value.

8. 8,<u>8</u>42 _____

9. 481.<u>5</u>6 _____

10. 0.0<u>0</u>83 _____

Middle-Grade Math Minutes © 2000 Creative Teaching Press

MINUTE 24

NAME _____

1. Ten cats have _____ legs in all.

2. $(8 - 3 \times 2)^2 =$

3. $0.84 \times 10 =$

4. $8.23 \times 10^2 =$

5. $25 \times 0.1 =$

6. If $a = 5$ and $b = 4$, then $ab =$

7. If $a = 2$ and $b = 3$, then $aba =$

Use <, >, or = to complete questions 8–10.

8. 4.03 _____ 4.01

9. 5.62 _____ 8

10. 6 _____ -5

MINUTE 25

NAME _____

1. $2(5)(3) =$

2. $0.04 \times 10^2 =$

3. Circle the greatest number: 4.8   4.08   4.008

4. Circle the number with the least value: 2.2   0.02   0.2

5. $4.68 \times 0.1 =$

Use <, >, or = to complete questions 6 and 7.

6. 3^2 _____ 4^2

7. 3^2 _____ 2^3

For questions 8–10, round to the underlined place value.

8. 4.0<u>8</u>1 _____

9. 20.<u>6</u>5 _____

10. <u>4</u>,348 _____

Middle–Grade Math Minutes © 2000 Creative Teaching Press

MINUTE 26

NAME _____

1. 75
   $\underline{\times\ 75}$

2. $|-11| =$

3. $3.26 \times 10 =$

4. $4.28 \times 0.1 =$

5. If $a = 2$ and $b = 7$, then $b^a =$

6. $8 - 2 + 4 =$

7. $10^3 =$

Use <, >, or = to complete questions 8–10.

8. 14.2 _____ 14.01

9. 0.043 _____ 0.5

10. 4^2 _____ 2^4

Middle-Grade Math Minutes © 2000 Creative Teaching Press

MINUTE 27

NAME _____

1. 2(4)(3) =

2. 1, 3, 6, 10, _____, _____, _____

3. Identify the <u>range</u> of the following numbers: 8, 2, 10, 4, 4, 6. _____

4. $\dfrac{3 + 2 + 1}{3}$ =

5. What is seven and twenty-six one hundredths rounded to the nearest whole number? _____

6. Eight birds have _____ wings in all.

7. Write 0.98989898... using bar notation. _____

8. 5 + 1.2 =

9. 0.403 x 1,000 =

10. Three thousand people plus two thousand people equal _____ people.

Middle-Grade Math Minutes © 2000 Creative Teaching Press

MINUTE 28

NAME _____

1. Circle the greatest number: 0.002   0.0021   0.019

2. Identify the range of the following numbers: 4, 3, 3, 15, 28. _____

3. $\dfrac{5 - 2 + 5}{2} =$

4. Two and a half hours later than 3:30 is _____.

5. What is the mean of 2, 7, and 9? _____

6. If $a = 4$, then $a^2 =$

7. What is the quotient of 35 divided by 5? _____

Use <, >, or = to complete questions 8–10.

8. 3.2×10^2 _____ 0.32×10^3

9. 0.04 _____ 0.301

10. 3 dozen donuts _____ 30 donuts

MINUTE 29

NAME _____

1. Identify the <u>range</u> of the following numbers:
   100, 212, 215, 308, 303, 600. _____

2. Write 0.43333... using bar notation. _____

3. 0.5, 1, 1.5, _____, _____, _____

4. What is the <u>mean</u> of two and twelve? _____

5. Identify the <u>mode</u> of the following numbers:
   1, 1, 1, 2, 2, 3, 3, 3, 3, 3, 4, 7. _____

6. $95 - 5 =$

7. The <u>product</u> of four and eight is _____.

8. $3^2 = 2^3$ Circle: True or False

9. Is two dozen evenly divisible by three?   Circle: Yes or No

10. Two hours later than 11:30 is _____.

Middle-Grade Math Minutes © 2000 Creative Teaching Press

MINUTE 30

NAME _____

1. |−50| =

2. Identify the <u>mode</u> of the following numbers: 2, 5, 6, 6, 11, 19, 20. _____

3. What is the <u>range</u> of the numbers in problem 2? _____

4. $\dfrac{5 + 4 + 1}{3 + 1 + 1}$ =

5. One day less than three weeks is _____ days.

6. Round 18.94 to the nearest whole number. _____

7. Circle the number with the least value: 0.002   0.0019   0.0004

8. 2 x 0.4 =

9. Two snakes plus seven snakes equal _____ snakes.

10. Write twenty-three thousandths in decimal form. _____

MINUTE 31

NAME _____

1. Two centuries and 6 decades equal _____ years.

2. Write as a fraction the probability of rolling a 3 on a six-sided die. _____

3. Three hours later than 2:30 is _____.

4. Circle the answer that shows how much a seventh-grade student might weigh:
   a. 500 kilograms   b. 50 kilograms   c. 5 kilograms   d. 100 grams

5. Circle the greater number: 54 inches   or   5 feet

6. If $5x + 1 = 21$, then $x =$

7. $\frac{1}{2} \cdot 18 =$

8. $0.054 > 0.1$ Circle: True or False

9. Are these lines parallel or perpendicular? _____

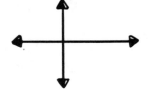

10. If you have read half of an 80-page book, how many pages have you read? _____

Middle-Grade Math Minutes © 2000 Creative Teaching Press

MINUTE 32

NAME _____

1. 42.6 x 100 =

2. If 8 + Ö = 12, then Ö =

3. 47 x 100 =

4. Is 21.49 closer to 21 or 22? _____

5. In 5 years, Lindsey will be a teenager. How old is she now? _____

6. If $\frac{?}{100}$ = 0.2, then ? =

7. Two quarters equal _____ nickels.

8. If 1 gallon has 4 quarts, how many quarts do 2 gallons have? _____

9. 1, 4, 9, 16, _____, 36, 49, 64

10. What is the probability of drawing a black marble from the bag? _____

MINUTE 33

NAME _____

1. $42.6 \div 100 =$

2. If $10 - \emptyset = 4$, then $\emptyset =$

3. $3 \times 6 = 18$ Which number is the <u>product</u>?_____

4. If $? \times 1 = 5 \times 2$, then $? =$

5. _____ days equal 48 hours.

6. Which digit in the number 95,184 is in the thousands place? _____

7. $2^3 - 3^1 =$

8. $4\overline{)5036}^{1259}$ Which number is the <u>divisor</u>? _____

9. If 5 circles weigh 10 pounds,
   how much does each square weigh? _____

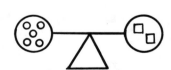

10. Name a prime number between 12 and 16. _____

MINUTE 34

NAME _____

1. Two days less than four weeks is _____ days.

2. Write twenty-six hundredths as a decimal. _____

3. Five triangles have _____ sides in all.

4. Circle the answer that shows the probability of the spinner stopping on red:
a. 1 out of 4   b. 1 out of 3
c. 2 out of 4   d. 2 out of 3

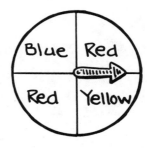

5. $|-25| =$

6. $\sqrt{16} =$

7. Circle the greatest number: 0.9   0.901   0.899

8. Five minutes less than an hour is _____ minutes.

9. Round 1,894 to the nearest hundred. _____

10. Circle the fraction that shows the chance of rolling an even number:
a. $\frac{1}{6}$ b. $\frac{2}{3}$ c. $\frac{3}{2}$ d. $\frac{1}{2}$

MINUTE 35

NAME _____

1. Circle the answer that shows how much a cow might weigh:
    a. 1,000 pounds   b. 1,000 grams   c. 1,000 tons

2. $10^2 =$

3. Six dollars equal _____ pennies.

4. Name the shape. _____

5. $\sqrt{49} =$

6. Four motorcycles have _____ wheels in all.

7. $4.78 \times 10^2 =$

8. $0.4 + 0.3 =$

9. $0.4 \times 0.3 =$

10. The <u>difference</u> between 11 and 3 is _____.

Middle-Grade Math Minutes © 2000 Creative Teaching Press

MINUTE 36

NAME _____

1. Is 372 evenly divisible by 2?   Circle: Yes or No

2. Name the shape. _____

3. $3 + 3 \cdot 3 + 3 =$

4. $\begin{array}{r} 23 \\ + 32 \\ \hline \end{array}$

5. $8^2 =$

6. $\sqrt{36} =$

7. Is 249 evenly divisible by 3?   Circle: Yes or No

8. If $a = 2$ and $b = 5$, then $ab =$

9. A <u>millipede</u> has _____ legs.

10. $0.004 \times 10^2 =$

MINUTE 37

NAME _____

1. Is 432 evenly divisible by 4?   Circle: Yes or No

2. $\sqrt{100}$ =

3. A <u>cent</u>ury has _____ years.

4. 0.4 + 0.6 =

5. 0.4 x 0.6 =

6. Circle the greater value: 0.5 or 0.$\bar{5}$

7. Name the shape. _____

8. Is 2,112 evenly divisible by 3?   Circle: Yes or No

9. If $a = 8$ and $b = 2$, then $\frac{a}{b}$ =

10. A <u>penta</u>gon has _____ sides.

Middle-Grade Math Minutes © 2000 Creative Teaching Press

MINUTE 38

NAME _____

1. Is 435 evenly divisible by 5?   Circle: Yes or No

2. Which is greater, 2 feet or 2 meters? _____

3. Twelve cars have _____ wheels in all.

4. Two feet are equal to _____ inches.

5. $7(4 + 5) =$

6. $968 \times 0.01 =$

7. $(0.8)(0.4) =$

8. Are the two lines parallel?   Circle: Yes or No

9. $0 \times 3{,}133 =$

10. Is this figure regular or not regular? _____

Middle-Grade Math Minutes © 2000 Creative Teaching Press

MINUTE 39

NAME _____

1. $0.0432 \times 10^3 =$

2. $10^2 \times 4.1 =$

3. Write $\frac{1}{2}$ as a decimal. _____

4. If $6{,}734 = 6.734 \times 10^a$, then $a =$

5. If eleven marbles are in each bag,
how many marbles are in 5 bags?_____

6. Name the shape. _____

7. Are these lines parallel?   Circle: Yes or No

Use <, >, or = to complete questions 8–10.

8. 1.78 _____ 1.774

9. 1.009 _____ 1.1

10. 10^2 _____ 1,000

Middle-Grade Math Minutes © 2000 Creative Teaching Press

MINUTE 40

NAME _____

1. A <u>deca</u>gon has _____ sides.

2. Eight squared equals _____.

3. The <u>mean</u> of 3, 5, 10 is _____.

4. $\sqrt{25} =$

5. Write $\dfrac{1}{4}$ as a decimal. _____

Use <, >, or = to complete questions 6–8.

6. 8.2 _____ 8.19

7. 0.006 _____ 0.08

8. 3^2 _____ $2 \cdot 2 \cdot 2$

For questions 9 and 10, round to the underlined place value.

9. 0.<u>6</u>83 _____

10. <u>8</u>8 _____

MINUTE 41

NAME _____

1. Write 64,120 in scientific notation. _____

2. If $a = 6$ and $b = 8$, then $ab =$

3. $11 \cdot 4 =$

4. $5 + 6 \cdot 2 =$

5. Nine squared is equal to _____.

6. The square root of 36 is _____.

7. Circle the answer that is equivalent to 0.432 x 0.14:
   a. 0.06   b. 6.048   c. 0.06048   d. 43.2

8. Name the shape. _____

For questions 9 and 10, round to the underlined place value.

9. 0.593 _____

10. 0.0032 _____

Middle-Grade Math Minutes © 2000 Creative Teaching Press

MINUTE 42

NAME _____

1. 25 + 50 =

2. Circle the answer that is equal to 0.62 x 0.4:
a. 0.04   b. 0.248   c. 8.3   d. 0.00083

3. 75
     x 75

4. Write 5,823 in scientific notation. _____

5. The <u>mean</u> of 2, 10, 9 is _____.

6. 0.5 + 0.2 =

7. A <u>pentomino</u> has _____ squares.

Use <, >, or = to complete questions 8–10.

8. 1.49 _____ 1.483

9. 3.43×10^4 _____ 3.43×10^5

10. 2.900 _____ 2.9

MINUTE 43

NAME _____

1. Is seventeen prime or composite? _____

2. Is 492 evenly divisible by 9?   Circle: Yes   or   No

3. Circle the answer that is equal to 2^2 x 3:
    a. 2 x 3   b. 3 x 3 x 2   c. 22 x 3   d. 2 x 2 x 3

4. 2^3 x _____ = 32

5. $\sqrt{49}$ =

6. 0.0836×10^3 =

7. Twenty dimes equal _____ dollars.

8. 1, 2, 4, 7, _____, _____, _____

9. 0.02 + 0.03 =

10. $16 \times \dfrac{1}{2}$ =

Middle-Grade Math Minutes © 2000 Creative Teaching Press

MINUTE 44

NAME _____

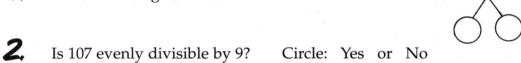

1. Factor 18 using the factor tree.

2. Is 107 evenly divisible by 9?   Circle: Yes or No

3. Twelve people have _____ ears in all.

4. $10^2 =$

5. Circle the answer that is equal to 0.046 x 0.3:
   a. 0.12   b. 0.0138   c. 0.128   d. 0.00463

6. If $a = 0.5$ and $b = 8$, then $ab =$

7. $\sqrt{16} =$

8. Write eight thousand four hundred thirty-six
   in scientific notation. _____

9. Is twenty-seven prime or composite? _____

10. Name the shape. _____

Middle-Grade Math Minutes © 2000 Creative Teaching Press

MINUTE 45

NAME _____

1. Forty-nine days equal _____ weeks.

2. $2 \times$ _____ $\times 5 = 70$

3. Round 17.9 to the nearest whole number. _____

4. Is 845 evenly divisible by 4?   Circle: Yes or No

5. $\frac{1}{4} = 0.20$ Circle: True or False

6. Multiply 100 and 1.82. _____

7. Complete the factor tree.

Use <, >, or = to complete questions 8–10.

8. 4.82 _____ 4.083

9. 3×2^2 _____ 2×3^2

10. 4,183 _____ 4.183×10^3

Middle-Grade Math Minutes © 2000 Creative Teaching Press

MINUTE 46

NAME _____

1. If $a = 8$ and $b = 2$, then $\dfrac{a}{b} =$

2. The mean of 1, 12, 14 is _____.

3. Two <u>cent</u>uries are equal to _____ years.

4. Circle the answer that is equivalent to 0.414141414...:
a. $0.4\overline{1}$ b. $0.41\overline{40}$ c. $0.\overline{41}$ d. $0.\overline{14}$

5. Five squared equals _____.

6. If $4{,}132 = 4.132 \times 10^a$, then $a =$

7. Is 7 prime or composite? _____

8. 2, 12, 22, 32, _____, _____, _____

9.
2.5
(2) (5)   Circle: True or False

10. What is one hundred divided by ten? _____

MINUTE 47

NAME _____

1. If $\frac{4}{16} = \frac{?}{4}$, then ? =

2. What fraction does the shaded portion of the box represent? _____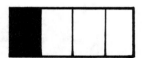

3. $\frac{52}{100}$ = _____ %

4. Two flags with 50 stars each have _____ stars in all.

5. If $\frac{4}{8} = \frac{?}{2}$, then ? =

6. $\frac{90}{100}$ = _____ %

7. $24 = 2 \cdot 2 \cdot 2 \cdot$ _____

8. In the number 54,631, what digit is in the ten thousands place? _____

9. Name the shape. _____

10. What is thirty plus thirty? _____

Middle-Grade Math Minutes © 2000 Creative Teaching Press

MINUTE 48

NAME _____

1. Multiply 0.023 and 10^2. _____

2. $\dfrac{41}{100} =$ _____ %

3. What fraction does the shaded portion of the box represent? _____

4. $44.68 \div 10 =$

5. $\sqrt{121} =$

6. If $a = 8$ and $b = 4$, then $ab =$

7. $2 \bullet 3 \bullet 5 =$

8. $0 \times 5{,}123 =$

9. $\dfrac{8}{10} =$ _____ %

10. If $\dfrac{1}{3} = \dfrac{m}{9}$, then $m =$

MINUTE 49

NAME _____

1. Is thirty-three prime or composite? _____

2. Write 76% as a decimal. _____

3. 1, 4, 7, 10, _____, _____, _____

4. $0.5 + 0.42 =$

5. $9^2 =$

6. What fraction does the shaded portion of the circle represent? _____

7. If $\dfrac{1}{7} = \dfrac{3}{n}$, then $n =$

8. $1.2 + 2.2 =$

9. The <u>sum</u> of 8 and 9 is _____.

10. Name the shape. _____

Middle-Grade Math Minutes © 2000 Creative Teaching Press

MINUTE 50

NAME _____

1. 6.2 x 10 =

2. If an ant has six legs, then how many legs do eight ants have in all? _____

3. List the factors of 12.
   _____, _____, _____, _____, _____, _____

4. (8 + 2)5 =

5. If $n - 8 = 2$, then $n =$

6. $5^2 =$

7. If $x = 2$ and $y = 6$, then $xy =$

8. $\pi = 3.1\_\_$

9. $0 \div 11 =$

10. Round eighteen and ninety-four hundredths to the nearest whole number. _____

MINUTE 51

NAME _____

1. $4^2 =$

2. If $36 = n^2$, then $n =$

3. Three hours from the time shown would be _____.

4. $7 + 3.4 =$

5. What are the first three multiples of 4? _____, _____, _____

6. List the factors of 20.

_____, _____, _____, _____, _____, _____

7. $8 \times$ _____ $= 96$

8. $\pi = 3.$ _____

9. _____ $\div 4 = 6$

10. If $5(n-2) = 35$, then $n =$

Middle-Grade Math Minutes © 2000 Creative Teaching Press

MINUTE 52

NAME _____

1. $9 \times 9 - 1 =$

2. Round 0.789 to the nearest tenth. _____

3. Use exponents to write $4 \times 4 \times 4 \times 4$. _____

4. $2 + 36 \div 6 =$

5. $140 \div 10 =$

6. $\pi =$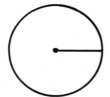

7. If $\frac{n}{3} = 2$, then $n =$

8. If $n = 2$, then $8n =$

Use <, >, or = to complete questions 9 and 10.

9. 1.34 _____ 1.308

10. 9^2 _____ 3^4

Middle-Grade Math Minutes © 2000 Creative Teaching Press

MINUTE 53

NAME _____

1. If $\dfrac{3}{5} = \dfrac{x}{50}$, then $x =$

2. List the first three multiples of 5. _____, _____, _____

3. $\dfrac{45}{100} =$ _____ %

4. If $n^2 = 64$, then $n =$

5. What are the factors of 18? _____, _____, _____, _____, _____, _____

6. $\dfrac{12}{4} =$

7. $2^2 \times 3 =$

8. If $a = 1$, $b = 2$, and $c = 3$, then $abc =$

9. Seventy-three out of 100 is _____ %

10. Is this a regular polygon?

Circle: Yes or No

Middle-Grade Math Minutes © 2000 Creative Teaching Press

MINUTE 54

NAME _____

1. Circle the answer that shows the
   probable length of this paperclip:
   a. 3 millimeters   b. 3 centimeters
   c. 3 meters   d. 3 kilometers

2. $4(2 + 3) =$

3. $0 \times 5,843 =$

4. $\pi =$

5. List the first three multiples of 10. _____, _____, _____

6. Is 13 prime or composite? _____

7. $16 = 3^2 \times 2$ Circle: True or False

8. If $16\% = \dfrac{?}{100}$, then ? =

9. Is 4,032 evenly divisible by 3?   Circle: Yes or No

10. What fraction does the shaded portion
    of the circle represent? _____

MINUTE 55

NAME _____

1. Eight out of 100 = _____ %

2. 18:100 is _____ %

3. What fraction does the shaded portion
of the box represent? _____

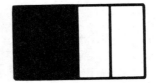

4.   65
   x 65

5. 10 x 8.4 =

6. Simplify: $\dfrac{18}{24}$ =

7. List the first three multiples of 9. _____, _____, _____

8. List the factors of 6. _____, _____, _____, _____

9. Is 432 evenly divisible by 9?   Circle: Yes or No

10. $3^2 \cdot 7 = 63$ Circle: True or False

Middle-Grade Math Minutes © 2000 Creative Teaching Press

MINUTE 56

NAME _____

1. $\sqrt{100} =$

2. 20:100 = _____ %

3. If $65\% = \dfrac{x}{100}$, then $x =$

4. Simplify: $\dfrac{8}{32} =$

5. What are the factors of 15? _____

6. List the first three multiples of 7. _____, _____, _____

7. Is 10,032 evenly divisible by 3?   Circle: Yes or No

Use <, >, or = to complete questions 8–10.

8. 10^2 _____ $\dfrac{1,000}{10}$

9. 0.042 _____ 0.05

10. 32% _____ 32:100

MINUTE 57

NAME _____

1. Simplify: $\dfrac{5}{15}$ =

2. Circle the greater number: 0.08   or   0.0763

3. If $a = 12$ and $b=100$, then $= \dfrac{a}{b}$ _____ %.

4. Is 509 evenly divisible by 4?   Circle: Yes or No

5. List the factors of 14. _____

6. List the first three multiples of 2. _____, _____, _____

7. Circle the answer that shows
the length of this ticket:
a. 4 km   b. 4 m
c. 4 cm   d. 4 mm

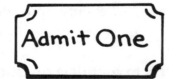

Use <, >, or = to complete questions 8–10.

8. 38% _____ 0.33

9. 3^2 _____ 2^4

10. $\dfrac{4}{16}$ _____ $\dfrac{1}{4}$

Middle-Grade Math Minutes © 2000 Creative Teaching Press

MINUTE 58

NAME _____

1. If $a = 1.2$ and $b = 10$, then $ab =$

2. If $\dfrac{12}{100} = \dfrac{?}{50}$, then ? =

3. List the factors of 24. _____

4. $0:100 =$ _____ %

5. $\dfrac{14}{2} =$

6. $\sqrt{36} =$

7. Circle the answer that shows
   the length of this pencil:
   a. 5 cm   b. 25 cm
   c. 50 cm   d. 75 cm

8. $4^2 =$

9. Four feet is equal to _____ inches.

10. Write twenty-three thousandths as a decimal. _____

MINUTE 59

NAME _____

1. Write 98% as a decimal. _____

2. Circle the greater value: 65% or $\dfrac{7}{10}$

3. 5.234 x 10 =

4. Round 8.546 to the nearest tenth. _____

5. 2^3 =

6. 10π =

7. If $\dfrac{6}{18} = \dfrac{?}{6}$, then ? =

8. Thirty-six eggs are equal to _____ dozen eggs.

9. Estimate: 8.2 + 4.9 =

10. What fraction does the shaded portion of the circle represent? _____

Middle-Grade Math Minutes © 2000 Creative Teaching Press

MINUTE 60

NAME _____

1. Write $\dfrac{35}{100}$ as a decimal. _____

2. $\dfrac{3}{4}$ = _____ %

3. If $\dfrac{1}{2} = \dfrac{s}{8}$, then s =

4. Circle the greater number: 0.049   or   0.08

5. Round 15.402 to the nearest tenth. _____

6. If $\dfrac{1}{3} = \dfrac{t}{60}$, then t =

7. Write 2:7 as a fraction. _____

8. If a = 100 and b = 0.06, then ab =

9. $0 \div 38$ =

10. Name the shape. _____

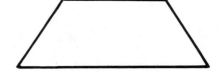

MINUTE 61

NAME _____

1. Write 0.12 as a percent. _____

2. Is 19 a prime number?   Circle: Yes or No

3. $\dfrac{1}{4}$ = _____ %

4. List the first three multiples of 5. _____, _____, _____

5. Round 14.9631 to the nearest tenth. _____

6. How many times must a three-minute timer be flipped to measure a half hour? _____

7. Is 817 evenly divisible by 4?   Circle: Yes or No

8. Circle the greater number: 4^2 or 8(3+4)

9. If 41,232 = 4.1232 x 10^m, then m =

10. Is twenty-four prime or composite? _____

Middle-Grade Math Minutes © 2000 Creative Teaching Press

MINUTE 62

NAME _____

1. 13,328.96 Which digit is in the hundredth place? _____

2. Circle the answer that is equal to v^6:
   a. $v + v + v + v + v + v$ b. $6v$ c. $v^3 + v^3$ d. $v \cdot v \cdot v \cdot v \cdot v \cdot v$

3. What is the temperature? _____

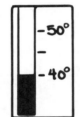

4. $\sqrt{25} =$

5. If $100 = 10^k$, then $k =$

6. $\dfrac{10}{2} =$

7. $3.38 \times 100 =$

8. What is the <u>sum</u> of two hundred and four hundred? _____

9. What is the smallest two-digit prime number? _____

10. $(2)(3)(4) =$

MINUTE 63

NAME _____

1. Circle the greater number: $\dfrac{3}{4}$ or 0.5

2. If $a = 8$, then $a^2 =$

3. $\begin{array}{r} 514 \\ 18\overline{)9252} \end{array}$ Which number is the <u>divisor</u>? _____

4. $6(4 + 2) =$

5. $\sqrt{10 \cdot 10}$

6. $\dfrac{1}{4} + \dfrac{2}{4} =$

7. What is the total cost of an item priced \$4.95 if there is 5% sales tax?_____

Use <, >, or = to complete questions 8–10.

8. 0.0083 _____ 0.01

9. 2^3 _____ 5 + 3

10. 1,000,000 _____ one million

Middle-Grade Math Minutes © 2000 Creative Teaching Press

MINUTE 64

NAME _____

1. Reduce: $\dfrac{21}{28} =$

2. If $22.009 = 22 + \dfrac{?}{1{,}000}$, then ? =

3. List the factors of 8. _____

4. $12(3) =$

5. $\dfrac{1}{8} + \dfrac{2}{8} =$

6. Circle the measurement that shows the greatest length:
a. 15 inches   b. 2 feet   c. 25 centimeters   d. 1 meter

7. Is 312 evenly divisible by 3?   Circle: Yes or No

8. If $ab = 10$ and $b = 2$, then $a =$

9. $1^3 =$

10. $4 + 2.5 =$

MINUTE 65

NAME _____

1. Write 28% as a decimal. _____

2. The Least Common Multiple of four and five is _____.

3. Reduce: $\dfrac{5}{40} =$

4. $\dfrac{4}{10} =$ _____ %

5. If $ac = 20$ and $a = 10$, then $c =$

6. $\dfrac{3}{7} - \dfrac{1}{7} =$

7. $\sqrt{5 \bullet 5}$

8. List the factors of 25. _____

9. $0.40 + 0.05 =$

10. If $10w = 50$, then $w =$

Middle-Grade Math Minutes © 2000 Creative Teaching Press

MINUTE 66

NAME _____

1. $4^2 =$

2. $5 + 2(4+1) =$

3. If $5\frac{1}{2} = \frac{?}{2}$, then ? =

4. 1, 2, 4, 8 . . .   Circle: Arithmetic sequence   or   Geometric sequence

5. Write $\frac{1}{3}$ as a decimal. _____

6. Circle the greater number: $\frac{2}{3}$ or $\frac{7}{11}$

7. What is the area of the rectangle? _____ cm^2

6cm

9 cm

8. What is the perimeter of the rectangle
shown in question 7?   _____ cm

9. Circle the answer that is equal to 5.12888... :
a. $5.\overline{128}$ b. $5.\overline{12}$ c. $5.12\overline{88}$ d. $5.12\overline{8}$

10. Round 1,286 to the nearest hundred. _____

MINUTE 67

NAME _____

1. $0.4 + 0.7 + 0.3 =$

2. Is 80,100 evenly divisible by 3?   Circle: Yes or No

3. Eight weeks = _____ days

4. If $3\dfrac{2}{3} = \dfrac{?}{3}$, then ? =

5. Write $\dfrac{1}{4}$ as a decimal. _____

6. Write eight thousand one hundred twenty-three in scientific notation. _____

7. If $b = 10$ and $h = 2$, then $bh =$

8. What is the area of the rectangle? _____ m^2

9. What is the perimeter of the rectangle shown in question 8? _____ m

10. What is the diameter of the circle? _____ cm

6m

8 m

6cm

MINUTE 68

NAME _____

1. How many points ahead are the Eagles? _____

Basketball	
Eagles	46
Stars	32

2. 3, 4.5, 6, 7.5, _____, _____

3. $11 < a \leq 13$ What odd number does a equal? _____

4. $2^3 \times 3 =$

5. What is the area?_____

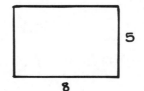

6. What is the perimeter of the rectangle shown in question 5? _____

7. $10.5 + \dfrac{1}{2} =$

8. If $\varpi \times 100 = 1{,}000$, then $\varpi =$

9. The absolute value of –7 is _____.

10. A negative number times a negative number is a _____.

MINUTE 69

NAME _____

1. If $l = 8$, $w = 2$, and $h = 1$, then $lwh =$

2. $6\overline{)48}$ with 8 above   Which is the <u>dividend</u>? _____

3. $3(2 + 3 + 1) =$

4. $0.244 \times 10 =$

5. 1 meter = 100 centimeters   Circle: True   or   False

6. What shape is a stop sign? _____

7. If $s = 3$, then $4s^2 =$

8. If $10w = 50$, then $w =$

9. What is the perimeter of the square? _____ cm
$\square$ 10 cm

10. What is the area of the square shown in question 9? _____ cm^2

Middle-Grade Math Minutes © 2000 Creative Teaching Press

MINUTE 70

NAME _____

1. Seven dollars is equal to _____ pennies.

2. Write $\frac{9}{4}$ as a mixed number. _____

3. Write $\frac{3}{4}$ as a decimal. _____

4. $0.2 + 0.25 =$

5. If $a = 3$ and $b = 9$, then $\frac{b}{a} =$

6. $24 \cdot \frac{1}{2} =$

7. $\left(\frac{1}{7}\right)\left(\frac{1}{8}\right) =$

8. What is the perimeter of the rectangle? _____

9. What is the area of the rectangle shown in question 8? _____

10. Area is always measured in what kind of units? _____

MINUTE 71

NAME _____

1. $0.046 \times 10^2 =$

2. If $w = 2$, then $5w^2 =$

3. $\frac{1}{2}(4 + 2) =$

4. $4 + 3 \cdot 2 =$

5. $\frac{1}{2} \times \frac{2}{7} =$

6. What is the perimeter of this shape? _____

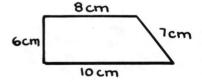

7. The <u>product</u> of 6 and 7 equals _____.

8. What is the reciprocal of $\frac{4}{9}$? _____

9. Write $\frac{13}{4}$ as a mixed number. _____

10. Write $\frac{1}{4}$ as a decimal. _____

Middle-Grade Math Minutes © 2000 Creative Teaching Press

MINUTE 72

NAME _____

1. $52 \times 10^2 =$

2. If $a = \dfrac{1}{2}$ and $b = \dfrac{1}{3}$, then $ab =$

3. $\dfrac{1}{2}(4 \cdot 2) =$

4. What is the reciprocal of $\dfrac{7}{5}$? _____

5. Reduce: $\dfrac{12}{36} =$

6. Write $5\dfrac{1}{4}$ as an improper fraction. _____

7. What is the perimeter of the triangle? _____

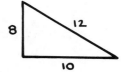

8. Write $\dfrac{1}{3}$ as a decimal. _____

9. What is the area of a box that is eight by four by two? _____

10. 10, 13, 16, 19. . .   Circle: Arithmetic sequence or Geometric sequence

MINUTE 73

NAME _____

1. Reduce: $\dfrac{3}{12} =$

2. $\dfrac{8}{12} = \dfrac{2}{3}$ Circle: True or False

3. If $6c = 42$, then $c =$

4. $(-8)(-4) =$

5. $5 - (-8) =$

6. If $-4a = -20$, then $a =$

7. Write 12% as a decimal. _____

8. What is the area of the rectangle? _____

7km

5km

9. What is the perimeter of the rectangle shown in question 8? _____

10. The square root of 36 is _____.

Middle-Grade Math Minutes © 2000 Creative Teaching Press

MINUTE 74

NAME _____

1. Simplify: $\dfrac{3}{6} =$

2. If $(-6)(-4) = b$, then $b =$

3. If $l = 2$, $w = 3$, and $h = 4$, then $lwh =$

4. What is the area of this shape? _____

    4

    12

5. Are the lines perpendicular? Circle: Yes or No

6. Two hours equal _____ minutes.

7. Round 18.24 to the ones place. _____

8. $12 - (-4) =$

9. $-4 + -5 =$

10. If $x - 2 = 3$, then $x =$

MINUTE 75

NAME _____

1. $\frac{1}{2}(16) =$

2. Round 0.3644 to the thousandths place. _____

3. If $x + 4 = 6$, then $x =$

4. How many degrees is angle x? _____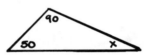

5. What quadrant is the point (–4, 4) in? _____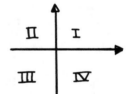

6. If $-8x = 24$, then $x =$

7. Draw the line(s) of symmetry for the letter: **H**

8. $7^2 =$

9. The square root of sixteen is _____.

10. $5\% = 0.5$ Circle: True or False

Middle-Grade Math Minutes © 2000 Creative Teaching Press

MINUTE 76

NAME _____

1. What quadrant is the point (–4, –7) in? _____

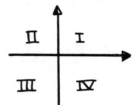

2. A triangle has _____ degrees.

3. Draw the line(s) of symmetry for the letter: **T**

4. Reduce: $\frac{9}{21}$ =

5. What kind of angle is this?
   Circle: Acute Obtuse Right

6. 4 – (–3) =

7. Three hours later than nine o'clock is _____.

8. If $a = 10$, then a^2 =

9. 13 x 3 =

10. List the factors of 15. _____

Middle-Grade Math Minutes © 2000 Creative Teaching Press

MINUTE 77

NAME _____

1. What quadrant is the point $(-4, 5)$ in? _____

$$
\begin{array}{c|c}
\text{II} & \text{I} \\
\hline
\text{III} & \text{IV}
\end{array}
$$

2. The square root of 64 is _____.

3. If $b^2 = 81$, then $b =$

4. Squares and square roots are the same thing.
Circle: True   or   False

5. $\dfrac{12}{2} =$

6. Seven squared =

7. Circle the answer that shows 8 times a number:
a. $8 + n$ b. $\dfrac{n}{8}$ c. $n - 8$ d. $8n$

8. List the factors of 18. _____

9. Perpendicular lines never intersect.   Circle: True   or   False

10. $10(4 + 2) - 10 =$

Middle-Grade Math Minutes © 2000 Creative Teaching Press

MINUTE 78

NAME _____

1. What is the area of the rectangle? _____

   5cm
   8cm

2. What is the reciprocal of $\frac{8}{11}$? _____

3. $\left(\frac{1}{4}\right)\left(\frac{1}{3}\right) =$

4. Circle the answer that shows 8 divided by a number:
   a. $8 \bullet n$ b. $8n$ c. $8(n)$ d. $\frac{8}{n}$

5. If $a = 25$, then $\sqrt{a} =$

6. What is the perimeter of this shape? _____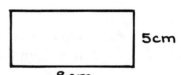

7. What is the shape shown in question 6 called? _____

8. What is the <u>mean</u> of two, five, and eleven? _____

9. What is the <u>product</u> of four and nine? _____

10. $43.2 \div 100 =$

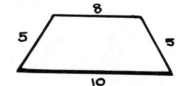

85

MINUTE 79

NAME _____

1. One thousand nine hundred ninety-nine minus one thousand nine hundred ninety-eight is _____.

2. Identify which of these numbers is a multiple of 5 and 6: 10, 15, 18, 24, 30

3. Round 15.132 to the nearest hundredth. _____

4. Circle the fraction that represents the least value: $\frac{1}{7}$ $\frac{1}{3}$ $\frac{1}{10}$

5. $246\overline{)76752}^{\,312}$ Which number is the <u>divisor</u>? _____

6. If 30 – ? = 15, then ? =

7. What is the area of the square? _____

5m

8. What is the perimeter of the square shown in question 7? _____

9. –8 + (–6) =

10. (–8)(–6) =

MINUTE 80

NAME _____

1. Circle the answer that shows how many hours Martha probably slept last night:
a. 24   b. 30   c. 19   d. 8

2. Four quarters and three dimes is how much money? _____

3. Circle the answer that shows 15 more than a number:
a. $y + 15$ b. $15y$ c. $\dfrac{15}{y}$ d. $y - 15$

4. What is the area of this shape? _____

5. Jon picks eight apples, eats three of them, and then picks two more. How many apples does he have now? _____

6. Circle the answer that shows the height of this drawing:
a. 2 centimeters b. 25 centimeters
c. 6 feet   d. 20 inches

7. If $10 + ? = 30$, then $? =$

8. Circle the numerator: $\dfrac{5}{11}$

9. $(-7)(-6) =$ **10.** $-5 + (-6) =$

MINUTE 81

NAME _____

1. $7 \times 8 \times 5 \times 0 \times 9 =$

2. What is the area of this shape? _____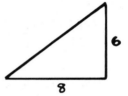

3. $\$1 - \$.56 =$

4. What is the perimeter of the rectangle? _____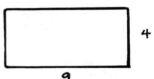

5. Circle all the numbers that have the same value:

0.5   5 $\frac{1}{2}$ $\frac{5}{10}$ 0.05   0.50

6. Three hours and seventy-five minutes is the same
as four hours and _____ minutes.

7. Shade 25% of this box.

8. How are two lines that are parallel to each other different from any other
two lines?

_____

9. Describe lines that are perpendicular to each other.

_____

10. $0.5(10) =$

Middle-Grade Math Minutes © 2000 Creative Teaching Press

MINUTE 82

NAME _____

1. 27 x 8 x 15 x 0 x 11 =

2. What is the area of the triangle? _____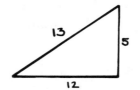

3. What is the perimeter of the triangle shown in question 2? _____

4. Multiply 2.46 by 100. _____

5. $1.39, $1.29, $1.19, _____, _____

6. Scott made six out of ten baskets. What percent is this? _____

7. Three weeks and two days equal _____ days.

8. What is the volume of this shape? _____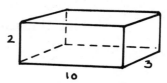

9. Which is longer? Circle: 10% of a mile   or   100% of a meter

10. Shade 75% of this box.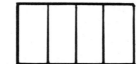

MINUTE 83

NAME _____

1. Farmer Brown has ten chickens. He sells all but four of them. How many chickens does he have left? _____

2. $3 + 4(2) =$

3. Twelve quarters equal _____ dollars.

4. 10% of 60 is _____.

5. $8^2 =$

6. Jo made eight out of ten baskets. What percent is this? _____

7. What is the area of a rectangle that is eight inches by five inches? _____

8. What is the volume of this shape? _____

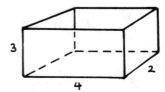

9. The absolute value of –12 is _____.

10. How many lines of symmetry does the letter **V** have? _____

Middle-Grade Math Minutes © 2000 Creative Teaching Press

MINUTE 84

NAME _____

1. In the number 923, how many tens are there? _____

2. Find n. $2 \cdot 8 - 4 = n$ $n =$

3. What is the volume of this shape? _____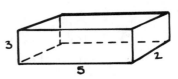

4. If $a = 64$, then $\sqrt{a} =$

5. Paula had thirty dollars in five-dollar bills. How many bills did she have? _____

6. Round 173 to the nearest ten. _____

7. What is the perimeter of a triangle with sides of eight cm, six cm, and one cm? _____

8. Find the area of a 5 m square. _____

9. Circle the product: 8 x 6 = 48

10. A pentagon has 6 sides.   Circle: True or False

MINUTE 85

NAME _____

1. What part of an hour is thirty minutes? _____

2. Are railroad tracks parallel or perpendicular? _____

3. Joe earns twenty-five cents each time he walks the dog. How much can he make in a week if he walks the dog twice each day? _____

4. Find n. $8 \times 4 = n$ $n =$

5. A rectangle has _____ sides and _____ angles.

6. Sue spent eighty-five cents on a candy apple. She gave the clerk one dollar. How much change did she receive? _____

7. One ton = _____ pounds

8. $7\overline{)14}$

9. $\sqrt{81} =$

10. $0 \cdot 1,000 =$

Middle-Grade Math Minutes © 2000 Creative Teaching Press

MINUTE 86

NAME _____

1. Round $26.59 to the nearest dollar.

2. Are the seat and the back of this chair parallel or perpendicular?_____

3. A triangle has _____ vertices.

4. There are _____ feet in one yard.

5. All the radii in a circle are the same length.   Circle: True or False

6. If $7(2 + n) = 21$, then $n =$

7. Is 46 evenly divisible by 2?   Circle: Yes or No

8. There are _____ hours in a day.

9. $8 - 3 + 3 =$

10. $4 \times 6 \times 1 =$

MINUTE 87

NAME _____

1. Water freezes at _____ °F.

2. 2 x 100 x 3 =

3. A cube has _____ faces.

4. A shape always has one line of symmetry.   Circle: True or False

5. What does the prefix *kilo* mean? _____

6. Write 13 x 13 x 13 using exponents. _____

7. Two radii equal one diameter.   Circle: True or False

8. (8 + 2) – (5 + 2) =

9. A letter used to represent an unknown number is called a _____.

10. The distance around a polygon is called the _____.

Middle-Grade Math Minutes © 2000 Creative Teaching Press

MINUTE 88

NAME _____

1. Round $46.28 to the nearest $10. _____

2. What number is 60,000 + 1,000 + 400 + 8? _____

3. Two tons equal _____ pounds.

4. Are lines that never intersect parallel or perpendicular? _____

5. One pound is _____ ounces.

6. Write the first 3 multiples of 8. _____, _____, _____

7. Is a house measured in meters or kilometers? _____

8. Estimate the sum for 2.9 + 3.2. _____

9. What fraction of an hour is 15 minutes? _____

10. Circle the prime number: 10   11   12   14   15

MINUTE 89

NAME _____

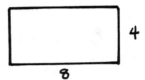

1. What is the area of the rectangle? _____

2. What number is 5,000 + 300 + 40 + 2? _____

3. What is the reciprocal of $\frac{4}{11}$? _____

4. Write $5\frac{1}{2}$ as an improper fraction. _____

5. $10^3 =$

6. There are _____ months in a year.

7. What is the <u>mean</u> of 2, 4, and 6? _____

8. A bus travels at 50 miles per hour for 3 hours. How many miles did it go? _____

9. $8 - 2 + 4 =$

10. $0 \div 11 =$

Middle-Grade Math Minutes © 2000 Creative Teaching Press

MINUTE 90

NAME _____

1. What is the area of the rectangle? _____

.4

.9

2. GCF stands for what mathematical phrase?

_____

3. What shape is this? _____

4. One is a factor of every number.   Circle: True or False

5. If 7 x n = 42, then n =

6. What is 3 more than 5 x 3? _____

7. Add four to the product of two and ten. _____

Use <, >, or = to complete questions 8–10.

8. 2 tons _____ 4,132 pounds

9. kilometer _____ meter

10. $\frac{1}{2}$(10) _____ 2(2.5)

MINUTE 91

NAME _____

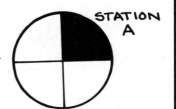

STATION A

1. What percentage of people like Station A? _____

2. Reduce: $\dfrac{10}{35} =$

3. $9^2 =$

4. If $b^2 = 16$, then $b =$

5. $10(4 + 3) =$

6. If $10\% = \dfrac{?}{100}$, then ? =

7. My book has 120 pages. If I have read half of it, how many pages have I read? _____

8. 998,104   Which digit is in the thousands place? _____

9. $0.003 + 0.0005 =$

10. What is the <u>product</u> of six and eight? _____

Middle-Grade Math Minutes © 2000 Creative Teaching Press

MINUTE 92

NAME _____

1. What is the Least Common Denominator of $\frac{1}{3}$ and $\frac{1}{5}$? _____

2. One gallon equals _____ quarts.

3. List the factors of 21. _____

4. $\frac{5}{9} + \frac{1}{9} =$

5. If you flip a coin, what is the probability of getting tails? _____

6. If you have eight boxes of crayons and ten crayons per box, how many crayons are there in all? _____

7. What percent does the shaded portion of the box represent? _____

8. If $a = 4$ and $b = 4$, then $ab = a^2$.   Circle: True or False

9. *Huck Finn* has 180 pages. If I have read one quarter of it, how many pages have I read? _____

10. Twenty percent is equal to what decimal? _____

MINUTE 93

NAME _____

1. Circle the greater number: $\dfrac{4}{7}$ or $\dfrac{6}{10}$

2. $\dfrac{1}{5} + \dfrac{1}{5} =$

3. Circle the answer that is equivalent to 30%:
   a. $\dfrac{3}{100}$ b. $\dfrac{3}{10}$ c. $\dfrac{3}{5}$ d. $\dfrac{1}{3}$

4. The Least Common Denominator of $\dfrac{1}{2}$ and $\dfrac{1}{8}$ is _____.

5. If $a = \dfrac{1}{2}$ and $b = 10$, then $ab =$

6. $42.381 \times 10^2 =$

7. Round 12,320 to the nearest hundred. _____

8. What is the <u>difference</u> between 8 and 14? _____

9. What score is shown on the dartboard? _____

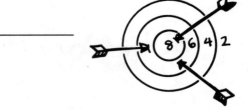

10. Simplify: $\dfrac{4}{20} =$

Middle-Grade Math Minutes © 2000 Creative Teaching Press

MINUTE 94

NAME _____

1. The Least Common Denominator of $\frac{1}{4}$ and $\frac{2}{5}$ is _____.

2. A single scoop of ice cream costs \$1.58. A double scoop costs \$1.80. How much more is the double scoop? _____

3. How much more liquid is needed to reach the 8 level? _____

4. List two ways you can make \$2.50 in change.

_____

_____

5. The absolute value of –22 is _____.

6. 1 kilometer = _____ meters

7. Circle the greater number: 2^8 or 8^2

8. 4 weeks = _____ days

9. Circle the composite numbers: 4   5   8   9   11

10. Reduce: $\frac{4}{24}$ =

MINUTE 95

NAME _____

1. If $3(4 + 2) = 2 \cdot 5 + ?$, then **?** =

2. What speed is shown on the speedometer? _____

3. The <u>sum</u> of 8 and 14 is _____.

4. What is the diameter of the circle? _____

5. 1^{17} =

6. Write $\frac{13}{5}$ as a mixed number. _____

7. What is the largest multiple of 5 that is less than 24? _____

8. $200 \div 100$ =

9. If $3(1 + m) = 15$, then m =

10. An octagon has _____ sides.

Middle-Grade Math Minutes © 2000 Creative Teaching Press

MINUTE 96

NAME _____

1. What is the radius of the circle? _____

2. 10^8 is the same as 1 followed by _____ zeros.

3. If $10,000 = 10^k$, then $k =$

4. 1, 7, 13, 19, _____, _____, _____

5. $\frac{2}{3} \times 1\frac{1}{2} =$

6. If $s\overline{)15}^{\,1}$, then $s =$

Use <, >, or = to complete questions 7–10.

7. 5 weeks _____ 1 month

8. 3 feet _____ 1 yard

9. $\frac{1}{2}$ _____ $\frac{1}{3}$

10. $3\frac{1}{2}$ _____ $\frac{7}{2}$

MINUTE 97

NAME _____

1. $(3 \times 1{,}000) + (2 \times 100) + (5 \times 10) =$

2. If $\dfrac{3}{4} = \dfrac{j}{8}$, then $j =$

3. $3 + 4 \cdot 6 =$

4. If $ab = 20$ and $a = 4$, then $b =$

5. Write $3\dfrac{1}{3}$ as an improper fraction. _____

6. How many centimeters of rain were there in March? _____

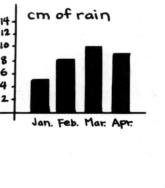

7. $\dfrac{32}{(4 \times 2)} \times 4 =$

8. Ten <u>centuries</u> equal _____ years.

9. Circle the prime numbers: 2   3   8   11   13

10. If $a = 8$, then $a^2 =$

MINUTE 98

NAME _____

1. $(5 \times 1,000) + (6 \times 10) =$

2. If the train left at 5:48 p.m. and arrived at 6:20 p.m., how long was the trip? _____

3. How many wheels are on the train shown in question 2? _____ (Remember to count both sides.)

4. Circle the numerator: $\dfrac{3}{8}$

5. What is the <u>mean</u> of 3, 7, 17? _____

6. $\dfrac{1}{5} =$ _____ %

7. $\sqrt{49} =$

8. If $\dfrac{?}{1000} = 0.019$, then $? =$

9. $\dfrac{1}{2} \cdot 12 =$

10. 48 inches = _____ feet

MINUTE 99

NAME _____

1. $\frac{1}{3} \times \frac{2}{5} =$

2. $\left(\frac{1}{2}\right)\left(\frac{1}{4}\right) =$

3. If $a = 2$ and $b = 4$, then $\frac{a}{b} =$

4. Write $5\frac{1}{2}$ as an improper fraction. _____

5. $0.3 + 0.4 =$

6. Circle the greater number: $\frac{3}{4}$ or $\frac{3}{5}$

7. Write $\frac{1}{2}$ as a decimal. _____

8. When the time is 8:10, the minute hand is on the _____.

9. $\frac{43}{100} \times 100 =$

10. If three people are sharing this pizza, how many pieces will each person get? _____

Middle-Grade Math Minutes © 2000 Creative Teaching Press

MINUTE 100

NAME _____

1. Circle the answer that shows about how long your bed is:
   a. 2 centimeters   b. 6 centimeters   c. 1 meter   d. 2 meters

2. $1\frac{1}{2}$ hours = _____ minutes

3. $(-4) + (-7) =$

4. 16, 14, 12, 10, 8, 4, 2   What number is missing? _____

5. Circle the greater number: 0.005   or   0.5

6. 32 ounces = _____ pounds

7. 14 is how many more than a dozen? _____

8. The <u>product</u> of eight and one is more than the <u>sum</u> of these two numbers.
   Circle: True or False

9. Circle the answer that shows which letter has 1 line of symmetry:
   a. **O**   b. **R**   c. **E**   d. **S**

10. What does 3 to the second power equal? _____

Minute Answer Key

Minute 1
1. 18
2. 16
3. 5
4. 2
5. 12
6. 7
7. 15, 18, 21
8. 14
9. >
10. <

Minute 2
1. 15
2. 400
3. 12
4. 10
5. 3
6. 16, 20, 24
7. 0
8. 16
9. 12
10. 9

Minute 3
1. 24
2. 0
3. 8, 4, 7
4. 2
5. 12
6. 10
7. 15
8. 50 cents or 50¢
9. 7
10. 4

Minute 4
1. 17, 21, 25
2. 2
3. 6
4. 84
5. sports
6. 17
7. 5
8. 12
9. 3
10. 6

Minute 5
1. 10
2. 2½
3. 16
4. 4
5. 32
6. 7
7. 16, 32, 64
8. 15
9. 6
10. 1

Minute 6
1. 16
2. 25
3. 8
4. 11
5. 0
6. 36
7. 1
8. 2
9. c
10. 8

Minute 7
1. 64
2. 10
3. 7
4. 13
5. 18
6. 100
7. 5
8. 6
9. a
10. 2

Minute 8
1. 9
2. 6
3. d
4. 7
5. 21
6. 4
7. 1,225
8. 6
9. 10
10. 10

Minute 9
1. 49
2. 6
3. 5
4. 30
5. 14
6. 17
7. 2,025
8. 8
9. 5
10. 72

Minute 10
1. 10
2. 5
3. 64
4. 9
5. 25
6. 8, 4, 2
7. 0
8. 10
9. 10
10. 2

Minute 11
1. 4
2. 8
3. 56
4. 18
5. 20
6. 6
7. 2,500
8. 64
9. 15
10. 3:00

Minute 12
1. 16
2. 12
3. 25
4. 8
5. 9
6. 16
7. 2
8. 500
9. 25
10. 28

Minute 13
1. 21
2. 54
3. 6
4. 28
5. 0
6. 80
7. 6
8. 3
9. 45
10. 3

Minute 14
1. 9
2. 5
3. 27
4. 100
5. 81
6. 8
7. 2
8. <
9. >
10. =

Minute 15
1. 16
2. 50
3. 6
4. 4,900
5. 18
6. 5
7. 25, 36, 49
8. 5
9. 15
10. 35

Minute 16
1. 32
2. 4,225
3. 120
4. 300
5. 25
6. 15
7. 15
8. 12
9. 3
10. 45

Minute 17
1. 49
2. 8
3. 0.9
4. 42
5. 6
6. 9:00
7. 3
8. <
9. <
10. =

Minute 18
1. 21
2. 0.052, 0.52, 5.2
3. 8
4. 5
5. 0.09
6. b
7. 88
8. >
9. <
10. =

Minute 19
1. 0.3
2. 0.55
3. 0.029
4. 81
5. 9
6. 36
7. 21
8. 0.08, 0.8, 8.0
9. 12
10. 24

Minute 20
1. 8
2. 8.20
3. 0.6
4. 26
5. 3
6. 0.02
7. 15.5
8. 16
9. 5
10. 4

Middle-Grade Math Minutes © 2000 Creative Teaching Press

MINUTE ANSWER KEY

MINUTE 21
1. 1.4
2. 18
3. 0.05
4. 70
5. 6
6. 11
7. 32
8. 0.8
9. 0.5
10. 3

MINUTE 22
1. 3,025
2. 9
3. 4
4. 48
5. 7
6. 22
7. 8
8. 17
9. 15
10. 56

MINUTE 23
1. 16
2. 18
3. b
4. 40
5. <
6. =
7. <
8. 8,800
9. 481.6
10. 0.01

MINUTE 24
1. 40
2. 4
3. 8.4
4. 823
5. 2.5
6. 20
7. 12
8. >
9. <
10. >

MINUTE 25
1. 30
2. 4
3. 4.8
4. 0.02
5. 0.468
6. <
7. >
8. 4.08
9. 20.7
10. 4,000

MINUTE 26
1. 5,625
2. 11
3. 32.6
4. 0.428
5. 49
6. 10
7. 1,000
8. >
9. <
10. =

MINUTE 27
1. 24
2. 15, 21, 28
3. 8
4. 2
5. 7
6. 16
7. $0.\overline{98}$
8. 6.2
9. 403
10. 5,000

MINUTE 28
1. 0.019
2. 25
3. 4
4. 6:00
5. 6
6. 16
7. 7
8. =
9. <
10. >

MINUTE 29
1. 500
2. $0.4\overline{3}$
3. 2, 2.5, 3
4. 7
5. 3
6. 90
7. 32
8. False
9. Yes
10. 1:30

MINUTE 30
1. 50
2. 6
3. 18
4. 2
5. 20
6. 19
7. 0.0004
8. 0.8
9. 9
10. 0.023

MINUTE 31
1. 260
2. ⅙
3. 5:30
4. b
5. 5 feet
6. 4
7. 9
8. False
9. Perpendicular
10. 40

MINUTE 32
1. 4,260
2. 4
3. 4,700
4. 21
5. 8
6. 20
7. 10
8. 8
9. 25
10. ⁴⁄₁₀, 4:10, ⅖, or 2:5

MINUTE 33
1. 0.426
2. 6
3. 18
4. 10
5. 2
6. 5
7. 5
8. 4
9. 5 pounds
10. 13

MINUTE 34
1. 26
2. 0.26
3. 15
4. c
5. 25
6. 4
7. 0.901
8. 55
9. 1,900
10. d

MINUTE 35
1. a
2. 100
3. 600
4. Trapezoid
5. 7
6. 8
7. 478
8. 0.7
9. 0.12
10. 8

MINUTE 36
1. Yes
2. Pentagon
3. 15
4. 55
5. 64
6. 6
7. Yes
8. 10
9. 1,000
10. 0.4

MINUTE 37
1. Yes
2. 10
3. 100
4. 1
5. 0.24
6. $0.\overline{5}$
7. Hexagon
8. Yes
9. 4
10. 5

MINUTE 38
1. Yes
2. 2 meters
3. 48
4. 24
5. 63
6. 9.68
7. 0.32
8. No
9. 0
10. Not regular

MINUTE 39
1. 43.2
2. 410
3. 0.5
4. 3
5. 55
6. Rectangle
7. Yes
8. >
9. <
10. <

MINUTE 40
1. 10
2. 64
3. 6
4. 5
5. 0.25
6. >
7. <
8. >
9. 0.7
10. 90

Minute Answer Key

Minute 41
1. 6.412×10^4
2. 48
3. 44
4. 17
5. 81
6. 6
7. c
8. Trapezoid
9. 0.6
10. 0.003

Minute 42
1. 75
2. b
3. 5,625
4. 5.823×10^3
5. 7
6. 0.7
7. 5
8. >
9. <
10. =

Minute 43
1. Prime
2. No
3. d
4. 4
5. 7
6. 83.6
7. 2
8. 11, 16, 22
9. 0.05
10. 8

Minute 44
1. 9 → 3, 3 (factor tree)
2. No
3. 24
4. 100
5. b
6. 4
7. 4
8. 8.436×10^3
9. Composite
10. Square

Minute 45
1. 7
2. 7
3. 18
4. No
5. False
6. 182
7. 7
8. >
9. <
10. =

Minute 46
1. 4
2. 9
3. 200
4. c
5. 25
6. 3
7. Prime
8. 42, 52, 62
9. False
10. 10

Minute 47
1. 1
2. $\frac{1}{4}$
3. 52
4. 100
5. 1
6. 90
7. 3
8. 5
9. Pentagon
10. 60

Minute 48
1. 2.3
2. 41
3. $\frac{1}{6}$
4. 4.468
5. 11
6. 32
7. 30
8. 0
9. 80
10. 3

Minute 49
1. Composite
2. 0.76
3. 13, 16, 19
4. 0.92
5. 81
6. $\frac{3}{8}$
7. 21
8. 3.4
9. 17
10. Hexagon

Minute 50
1. 62
2. 48
3. 1, 2, 3, 4, 6, 12
4. 50
5. 10
6. 25
7. 12
8. 4
9. 0
10. 19

Minute 51
1. 16
2. 6
3. 11:00
4. 10.4
5. 0, 4, 8
6. 1, 2, 4, 5, 10, 20
7. 12
8. 14
9. 24
10. 9

Minute 52
1. 80
2. 0.8
3. 4^4
4. 8
5. 14
6. 3.14
7. 6
8. 16
9. >
10. =

Minute 53
1. 30
2. 0, 5, 10
3. 45
4. 8
5. 1, 2, 3, 6, 9, 18
6. 3
7. 12
8. 6
9. 73
10. Yes

Minute 54
1. b
2. 20
3. 0
4. 3.14
5. 0, 10, 20
6. Prime
7. False
8. 16
9. Yes
10. $\frac{3}{4}$

Minute 55
1. 8
2. 18
3. $\frac{1}{2}$
4. 4,225
5. 84
6. $\frac{3}{4}$
7. 0, 9, 18
8. 1, 2, 3, 6
9. Yes
10. True

Minute 56
1. 10
2. 20
3. 65
4. $\frac{1}{4}$
5. 1, 3, 5, 15
6. 0, 7, 14
7. Yes
8. =
9. <
10. =

Minute 57
1. $\frac{1}{3}$
2. 0.08
3. 12
4. No
5. 1, 2, 7, 14
6. 0, 2, 4
7. c
8. >
9. <
10. =

Minute 58
1. 12
2. 6
3. 1, 2, 3, 4, 6, 8, 12, 24
4. 0
5. 7
6. 6
7. a
8. 16
9. 48
10. 0.023

Minute 59
1. 0.98
2. $\frac{7}{10}$
3. 52.34
4. 8.5
5. 8
6. 31.4
7. 2
8. 3
9. 13
10. $\frac{2}{8}$ or $\frac{1}{4}$

Minute 60
1. 0.35
2. 75
3. 4
4. 0.08
5. 15.4
6. 20
7. $\frac{2}{7}$
8. 6
9. 0
10. Trapezoid

Middle-Grade Math Minutes © 2000 Creative Teaching Press

Minute Answer Key

Minute 61
1. 12%
2. Yes
3. 25
4. 0, 5, 10
5. 15.0
6. 10
7. No
8. 8(3+4)
9. 4
10. Composite

Minute 62
1. 6
2. d
3. 40°
4. 5
5. 2
6. 5
7. 338
8. 600
9. 11
10. 24

Minute 63
1. 3/4
2. 64
3. 18
4. 36
5. 10
6. 3/4
7. $5.20
8. <
9. =
10. =

Minute 64
1. 3/4
2. 9
3. 1, 2, 4, 8
4. 36
5. 3/8
6. d
7. Yes
8. 5
9. 1
10. 6.5

Minute 65
1. 0.28
2. 20
3. 1/8
4. 40
5. 2
6. 2/7
7. 5
8. 1, 5, 25
9. 0.45
10. 5

Minute 66
1. 16
2. 15
3. 11
4. Geometric sequence
5. $0.\overline{3}$
6. 2/3
7. 54
8. 30
9. d
10. 1,300

Minute 67
1. 1.4
2. Yes
3. 56
4. 11
5. 0.25
6. 8.123×10^3
7. 20
8. 48
9. 28
10. 12

Minute 68
1. 14
2. 9, 10.5
3. 13
4. 24
5. 40
6. 26
7. 11
8. 10
9. 7
10. positive number

Minute 69
1. 16
2. 48
3. 18
4. 2.44
5. True
6. Octagon
7. 36
8. 5
9. 40
10. 100

Minute 70
1. 700
2. 2 1/4
3. 0.75
4. 0.45
5. 3
6. 12
7. 1/56
8. 26
9. 30
10. square units

Minute 71
1. 4.6
2. 20
3. 3
4. 10
5. 1/7
6. 31 cm
7. 42
8. 9/4
9. 3 1/4
10. 0.25

Minute 72
1. 5,200
2. 1/6
3. 4
4. 5/7
5. 1/3
6. 21/4
7. 30
8. $0.\overline{3}$
9. 64
10. Arithmetic sequence

Minute 73
1. 1/4
2. True
3. 7
4. 32
5. 13
6. 5
7. 0.12
8. 35 km^2
9. 24 km
10. 6

Minute 74
1. 1/2
2. 24
3. 24
4. 48
5. No
6. 120
7. 18
8. 16
9. –9
10. 5

Minute 75
1. 8
2. 0.364
3. 2
4. 40
5. II
6. –3
7. 
8. 49
9. 4
10. False

Minute 76
1. III
2. 180
3. 
4. 3/7
5. Acute
6. 7
7. 12:00
8. 100
9. 39
10. 1, 3, 5, 15

Minute 77
1. II
2. 8
3. 9
4. False
5. 6
6. 49
7. d
8. 1, 2, 3, 6, 9, 18
9. False
10. 50

Minute 78
1. 40 cm^2
2. 11/8
3. 1/12
4. d
5. 5
6. 28
7. Trapezoid
8. 6
9. 36
10. 0.432

Minute 79
1. 1
2. 30
3. 15.13
4. 1/10
5. 246
6. 15
7. 25 m^2
8. 20 m
9. –14
10. 48

Minute 80
1. d
2. $1.30
3. a
4. 20
5. 7
6. a
7. 20
8. 5
9. 42
10. –11

MINUTE ANSWER KEY

MINUTE 81
1. 0
2. 24
3. $.44
4. 26
5. 0.5, ½, ⁵⁄₁₀, 0.50
6. 15
7.  ▢
8. Parallel lines never intersect.
9. Perpendicular lines form a ninety degree angle where they meet.
10. 5

MINUTE 82
1. 0
2. 15
3. 30
4. 246
5. $1.09, $0.99
6. 60%
7. 23
8. 60
9. 10% of a mile
10.

MINUTE 83
1. 4
2. 11
3. 3
4. 6
5. 64
6. 80%
7. 40 in.²
8. 24
9. 12
10. 1

MINUTE 84
1. 2
2. 12
3. 30
4. 8
5. 6
6. 170
7. 15 cm
8. 25 m²
9. 48
10. False

MINUTE 85
1. ½
2. Parallel
3. $3.50
4. 32
5. 4, 4
6. 15 cents

7. 2,000
8. 2
9. 9
10. 0

MINUTE 86
1. $27
2. Perpendicular
3. 3
4. 3
5. True
6. 1
7. Yes
8. 24
9. 8
10. 24

MINUTE 87
1. 32
2. 600
3. 6
4. False
5. 1,000
6. 13³
7. True
8. 3
9. variable
10. perimeter

MINUTE 88
1. $50
2. 61,408
3. 4,000
4. Parallel
5. 16
6. 0, 8, 16
7. Meters
8. 6
9. ¼
10. 11

MINUTE 89
1. 32
2. 5,342
3. 1¹⁄₄
4. 1½
5. 1,000
6. 12
7. 4
8. 150
9. 10
10. 0

MINUTE 90
1. 0.36
2. Greatest Common Factor
3. Semicircle
4. True
5. 6
6. 18

7. 24
8. <
9. >
10. =

MINUTE 91
1. 25%
2. ²⁄₇
3. 81
4. 4
5. 70
6. 10
7. 60
8. 8
9. 0.0035
10. 48

MINUTE 92
1. 15
2. 4
3. 1, 3, 7, 21
4. ⁶⁄₉ or ⅔
5. ½ or 1:2 or 50%
6. 80
7. 40%
8. True
9. 45
10. 0.2

MINUTE 93
1. ⁹⁄₁₀
2. ⅖
3. b
4. 8
5. 5
6. 4,238.1
7. 12,300
8. 6
9. 20
10. ⅕

MINUTE 94
1. 20
2. $.22
3. 3
4. Answers may vary.
5. 22
6. 1,000
7. 2⁸
8. 28
9. 4, 8, 9
10. ⅙

MINUTE 95
1. 8
2. 54
3. 22
4. 16
5. 1
6. 2⅗
7. 20
8. 2

9. 4
10. 8

MINUTE 96
1. 7
2. 8
3. 4
4. 25, 31, 37
5. ⁶⁄₆ or 1
6. 15
7. >
8. =
9. >
10. =

MINUTE 97
1. 3,250
2. 6
3. 27
4. 5
5. ¹⁰⁄₃
6. 10
7. 16
8. 1,000
9. 2, 3, 11, 13
10. 64

MINUTE 98
1. 5,060
2. 32 minutes
3. 10
4. 3
5. 9
6. 20
7. 7
8. 19
9. 6
10. 4

MINUTE 99
1. ²⁄₁₅
2. ⅛
3. ²⁄₄ or ½
4. 1½
5. 0.7
6. ¾
7. 0.5
8. 2
9. 43
10. 4

MINUTE 100
1. d
2. 90
3. –11
4. 6
5. 0.5
6. 2
7. 2
8. False
9. c
10. 9

Middle-Grade Math Minutes © 2000 Creative Teaching Press